Get Ready for School

BUMPER WORKBOOK

This workbook belongs to

Use pencils, crayons and stickers to complete the activities in this book. When there is a sticker missing, you will see this pattern:

At school

At school, you might have a cloakroom.
Colour and sticker this cloakroom picture.

Draw lines from the cloakroom to the things that you can store there.

coat

cow

backpack

helmet

piano

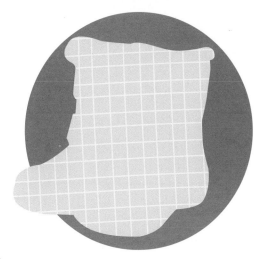

boots

Playing inside

Sometimes you will play inside.
Circle the playtime activities.
Cross out the things you don't do at playtime.

sleeping

reading

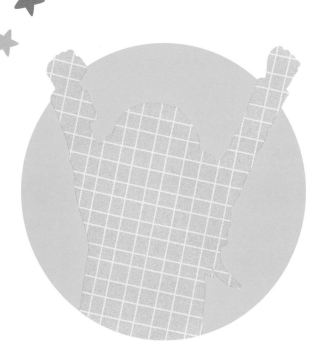

dressing up

taking a bath

building

playing with trains

painting

doing a jigsaw puzzle

Story time

A teacher might read you a story.
Colour and sticker this story-time picture.

What do you do when the teacher is reading?
Circle the correct picture.

talk to friends　　**listen to the story**

How do you ask a question? Circle the correct picture.

put up your hand　　**shut your eyes**

Snack time

Circle the things you might eat and drink at snack time.
Cross out the things you do not eat.

yogurt

bowl

hat

sandwich

apple

milk

chair

fruit juice

Nap time

At school, you might take a nap.
Sticker and colour the nap-time picture.

Wash your hands

Draw lines from the girl washing her hands to the times when you should wash your hands.

after using
the toilet

after reading

before eating

after getting
dirty

Making things

Match the things you use to make things with the pictures of children using them.

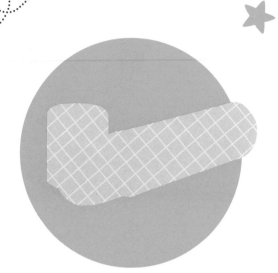

glue stick

drawing

crayons

sticking

modelling clay

cutting out

scissors

painting

paints

modelling

Making music

Match the musical instruments with the people using them.

drum

playing the recorder

recorder

playing a drum

piano

playing the xylophone

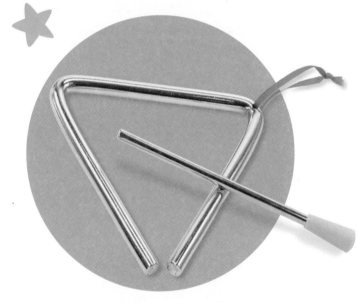

triangle

playing the triangle

xylophone

playing the piano

Playing outside

Circle the playtime activities you might do outside.
Cross out things you don't do when you play outside.

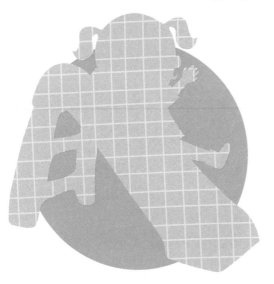

sliding

eat dinner

digging

climbing

swinging

riding

get a haircut

kicking

Nature table

Draw lines from the nature table to the things that belong there.

flowers

magnifying glass

socks

leaves and
cones

paints

Our nature
table!

shells

Home time

Circle the things you can take home from school.
Cross out the things you leave at school.

art

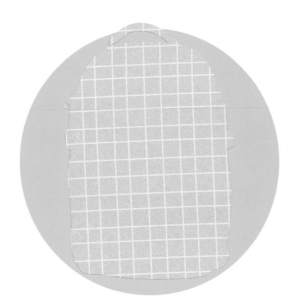

backpack

table

water bottle

coat

lunch box

teacher

Red and blue

Draw lines from the **red** things to the word **red**.
Draw lines from the **blue** things to the word **blue**.

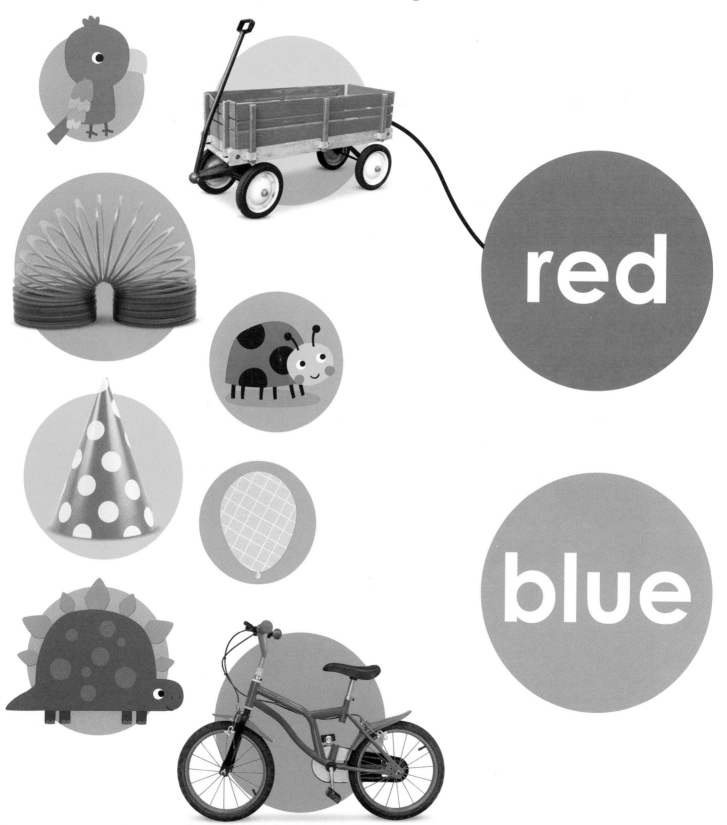

red

blue

Yellow and green

Put a **Y** by each yellow object.
Put a **G** by each green object.

Purple and orange

Draw lines from the **purple** things to the word **purple**.
Draw lines from the orange things to the word orange.

purple

orange

White and black

Put a **W** by each white object.
Put a **B** by each black object.

Where is it?

Sticker the dog **outside** the house.
Sticker the cat **inside** the house.

Colour the car that
is **in front** red.
Colour the car that
is **behind** blue.

High and low

Sticker the girl in the **top** bunk.
Sticker the boy in the **bottom** bunk.

Put an **H** by the monkey
that is up **high**.
Put an **L** by the monkey
that is down **low**.

Above and below

Sticker the teddy bear **on** the bed.
Sticker the shoes **under** the bed.

Draw a bird
above the boat.
Draw a fish
below the boat.

Signs to follow

Trace **stop** on the stop sign.
Trace **go** on the go sign.

Trace **up** on the arrow pointing up.
Trace **down** on the arrow pointing down.

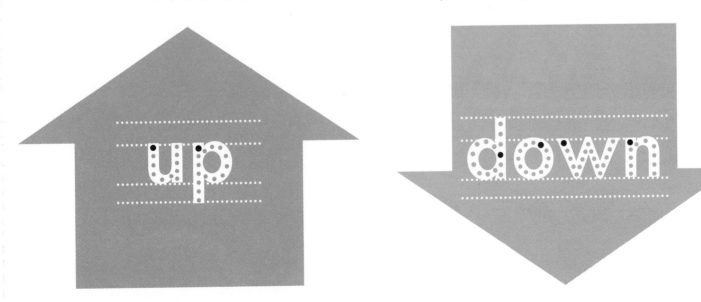

First and last

Put a tick ✔ by the car that came **first**.
Put a cross ✖ by the car that came **last**.

Tick ✔ the tree that is **nearby**.
Put a cross ✖ by the tree that is **far away**.

Size words

Circle the correct one in each box.

Circle the **big** dog.

Circle the **little** top.

Circle the **large** ball.

Circle the **small** insect.

More size words

Circle the correct one in each box.

Circle the **taller** boy.

Circle the **shorter** girl.

Circle the **longer** pencil.

Circle the **shorter** crayon.

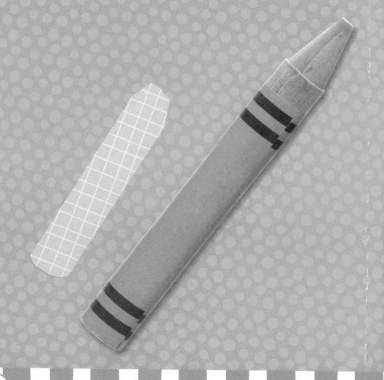

How much?

Circle the correct one in each box.

Circle the glass that is **full**.

Circle the jug that is **empty**.

Circle the jar with **more** sweets than the other.

Circle the plate with **less** cake than the other.

Weather words

Trace the weather words.

It is sunny.

It is raining.

It is cold.

It is windy.

Weather match

Draw lines to match each child to the weather.

sunny

raining

cold

windy

The seasons

Finish colouring the summer picture.

Finish colouring the autumn picture.

The seasons

Finish colouring the winter picture.

Finish colouring the spring picture.

Summer clothes

Circle the clothes Ben wears in **summer**.

coat

sandals

T-shirt

gloves

sunglasses

woolly hat

scarf

swimming shorts

Winter clothes

Circle the clothes Ella wears in **winter**.

jumper

hat

boots

scarf

coat

sunglasses

T-shirt

woolly hat

Happy or sad?

Circle the face that goes with the picture.

Match the emotions

Draw lines to match the faces to the emojis.

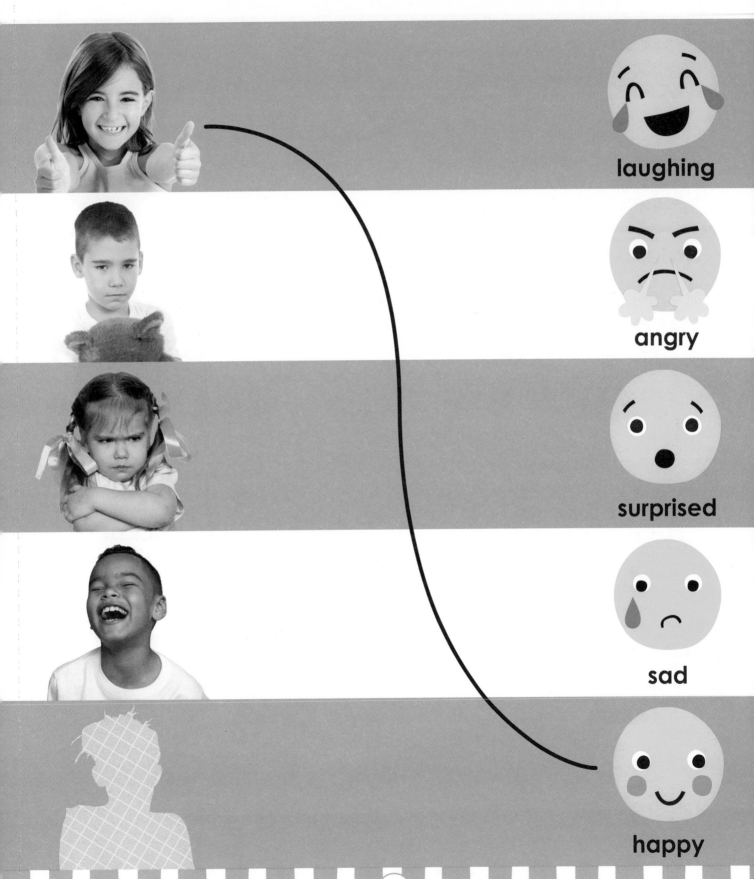

laughing

angry

surprised

sad

happy

School things

Circle the things you take to school.

water bottle

slippers

dog

lamp

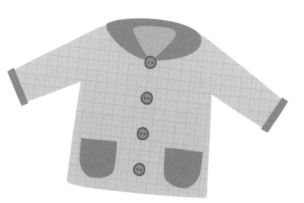

jacket

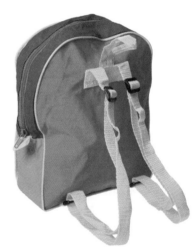

backpack

pencil

School days

Draw lines to match the objects to the activities.

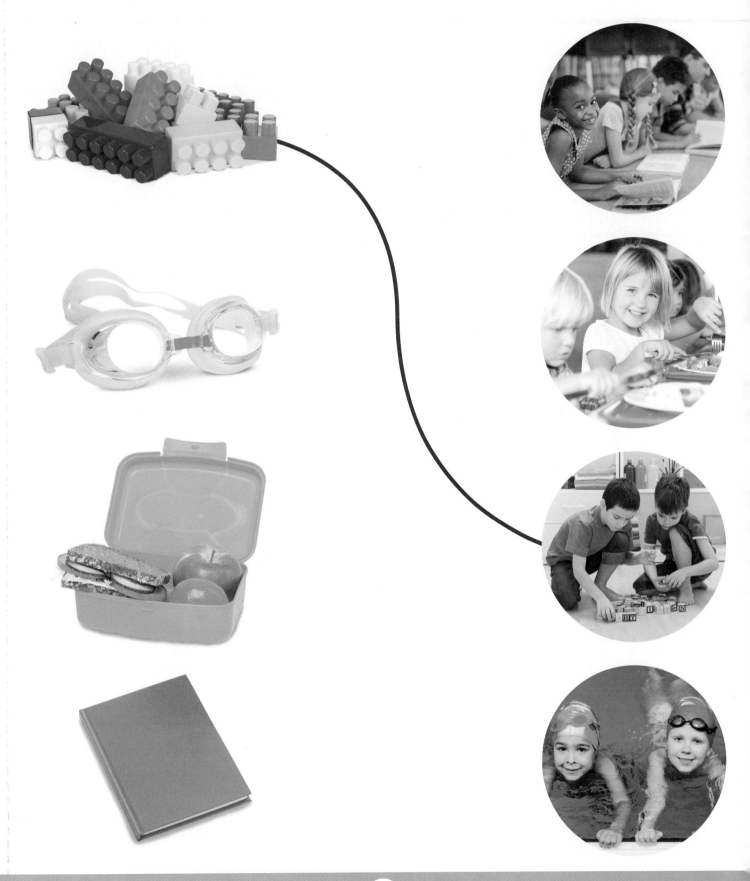

Uppercase letters

Circle the letters. One has been circled for you.

Lowercase letters

Circle the letters.

a ★ b d

s o w

h p

m k o

Find the words

Words are made up of letters joined together. Circle the words.

dog

go

is

me

big

fun

see

look

Find the words

Circle the words.

egg ⭐ play

was

hen

in

run

no

can

yes

Sort letters and words

Circle the words with a **red** pencil.
Circle the letters with a **blue** pencil.

bee   b   x

fish   j

u   bus

h   nose   f   cat

ball   car

k   w   moon

Find the letters

Draw a line from each letter in the word
to the same letter around it.

p i a

b——bird d

u

w r b

z t

v boat h

a o

m

49

Find uppercase letters

Find and circle the letter **S**.

R Z S B O Q

Spider

Find and circle the letter **L**.

K T C I L J

Lion

Find and circle the letter **O**.

Q D P O C G

Octopus

Find and circle the letter **F**.

Y R F T P E

Fish

Find lowercase letters

Find and circle the letter **h**.

t h b d k f

house

Find and circle the letter **m**.

n W x h m h

mouse

Find and circle the letter **v**.

W u v Z x y

vet

Find and circle the letter **d**.

h b d q k p

dog

51

Match the direction

Circle the **c**'s that face the correct way.

cow

Circle the **b**'s that face the correct way.

b d b d b

ball

Circle the **p**'s that face the correct way.

q p p q p

panda

Circle the **s**'s that face the correct way.

sock**s**

Match the direction

Circle the **g**'s that face the correct way.

g g g g g

goat

Circle the **f**'s that face the correct way.

f f f f f f

fox

Circle the **j**'s that face the correct way.

j j j j j j

jacket

Circle the **h**'s that face the correct way.

h h h h h h

hippo

Match uppercase letters

Draw lines to match the uppercase letters.

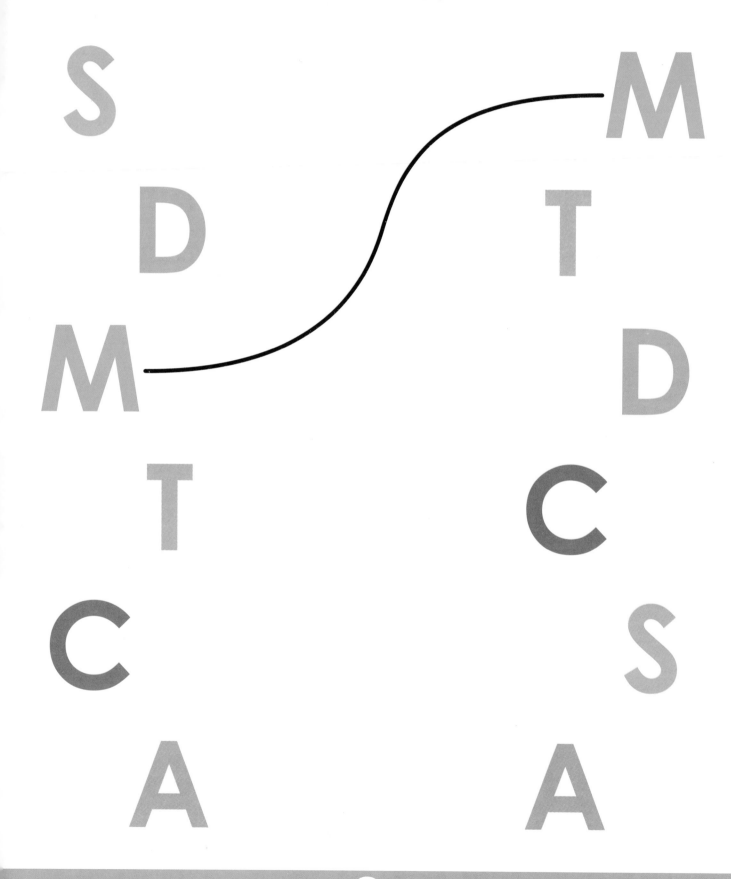

Match lowercase letters

Draw lines to match the lowercase letters.

b

g

n

b

g

k

e

v

k

v

e

n

Letter order

Circle the word **saw**. The letters must be in the correct order.

saw

was

saw

was

I **saw** a bird.

Circle the word **on**.

on on

no on

I am **on** a leaf.

Letter order

Circle the word **cat**.

cat
tac
act
cat

Circle the word **big**.

gib
big
big
gib

First words

Trace the words.

sun   dog   ball

car   cap   mug

First words

Trace the words.

star   drum   duck

leaf   dress   fish

Cars and buses

Draw lines from the **bus** words to the **bus**.
Draw lines from the **car** words to the **car**.

bus

bus

car

car

bus

bus

car

car

bus

car

Lions and tigers

Draw lines from the **lion** words to the **lion**.
Draw lines from the **tiger** words to the **tiger**.

lion   tiger

Match the words

Draw lines to match the words that are the same.

 owl

 fox

 tree

 bird

 deer

 owl

 bird

bee

 bee

tree

 fox

deer

Match the words

Draw lines to match the words that are the same.

 shell · whale

 shark · fish

 crab · shark

 fish · boat

 whale · crab

 boat · shell

Write sentences

Sentences are made up of words.
Trace the sentences.

I am a cat.

I am a dog.

I am a bat.

I am a frog.

Write sentences

Trace the sentences.

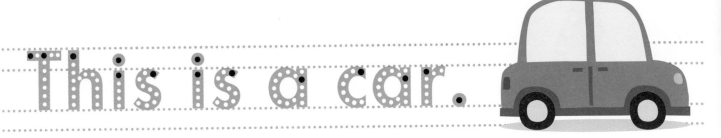

This is a car.

This is a king.

This is a star.

This is a ring.

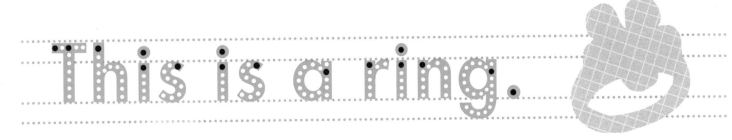

The uppercase letters

Trace the uppercase letters.

The lowercase letters

Trace the lowercase letters.

Congratulations!

GOOD WORK AWARD!

Name: ....

has successfully completed the

Get Ready for School

Bumper Workbook

Date: ....

Search this page for the stickers you need.

ALL ABOUT SCHOOL

Pages **2–3**

Page **4**

Page **6**

Page **9**

Page **10**

Pages **12–13**

Pages **14–15**

Pages **16–17**

Page **19**

Pages **20–21**

Search this page for the stickers you need.

VOCABULARY

Pages **22–23**

Pages **24–25**

Page **26**

Page **27**

Pages **30–31**

Pages **32–33**

Page **28**

Pages **34–35**

Page **38**

Pages **36–37**

Page **41**

Extra stickers

Search this page for the stickers you need.

Pages 44–45

Pages 46–47

Page 48

Pages 52–53

Pages 56–57

Pages 50–51

Pages 64–65

Pages 58–59

Pages 62–63

Page 61

Certificate Stickers